JOHN SMITH

Illustrated by Clare Beaton

These books are designed to give practice in spelling and to widen vocabulary.

The series contains picture puzzles, questions on groups of words containing the same sound and questions on general knowledge — each page is a challenge.

The words needed to answer the questions are jumbled up in the boxes and brackets, at the start of each section.

Only correct spellings should be counted.

There is a worked example on the inside back cover. Answers are given at the back of the book.

CONTENTS

a

bat	hat	rat
lad	bag	gas

1. It has four legs and a long tail ______ rat
2. It is used for hitting a ball ______ bat
3. Some Mums use this for cooking ______ gas
4. Another name for a boy ______ lad
5. This is worn on the head ______ hat
6. We put things in a — ______ bag

e

ten	peg	hen
leg	bed	pen

7. A bird ______ hen
8. We sleep in a — ______ bed
9. 10 ______ ten
10. To hang your coat on ______ peg
11. We use this to write with ______ pen
12. A part of the body ______ leg

i

pin	**hit**	**sit**
tin	**lip**	**bit**

1. A part of the mouth ______
2. This has a sharp point ______
3. Some foods come in a — ______
4. Chairs are used to — in ______
5. A piece ______
6. We — a nail with a hammer ______

o

hop	cot	log
top	dog	fog

7. A baby's bed ______
8. A pet ______
9. Mist ______

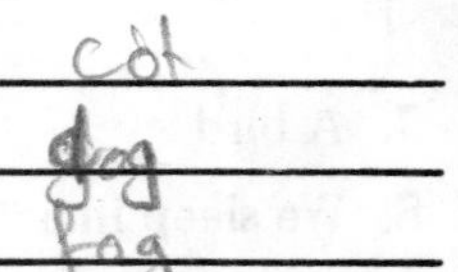

10. The girl tried to — on one leg ______
11. A piece of a tree ______
12. The cream is on the — of the milk ______

u

fun	bull	mug	
nut	hug	rub	cub

1. We can drink out of this mug
2. Throw your arms around a person hug
3. It grows on a tree nut
4. A farm animal bull
5. We do this when we polish something rub
6. A baby fox cub
7. He is always happy and full of — fun

y { why try fry cry dry }

8. Not wet dry
9. '— are you upset?' asked the teacher Why
10. We — to write neatly try
11. I like my Mum to — me an egg try
12. Tears came into his eyes and he began to — cry

ar

car tar bar
far jar star

1. For putting jam in ______
2. Play near the house, don't go — away ______
3. It twinkles in the sky ______
4. It has four wheels ______

5. Used for making roads ______
6. A metal rod ______

ow { owl drown howl bow tower flower

7. It has a stem and petals ______
8. A high building ______
9. To bend forward ______
10. The name of a bird ______
11. We may — in deep water ______
12. Dogs and wolves do this ______

On the farm

hen	cock	goat	dog
cat	barn	stack	
tractor	pond	duck	

1. stack
2. barn
3. duck
4. pond
5. tractor
6. cat
7. hen
8. cock
9. goat
10. dog

Score

er

her jerk fern term

1. Holidays come at the end of — term
2. A plant Jerk
3. She ate — dinner her
4. Pull sharply Fern

or { horns born worn corn storm form stork port }

5. A bird with long legs [illegible]
6. Rain and strong winds make a — Storm
7. It grows in the farmer's fields Corn
8. She was — in 1972 bor
9. A ship sails into this ~~form~~ stork
10. A bull has two of these horns
11. Susan has — this dress for a long time Worn
12. Which — are you in at school? pork

fir	**bird**	**shirt**
stir	**girl**	**first**

1. A sparrow is a — bird
2. A tree with leaves like needles fir
3. When we make gravy we — it stir
4. The — wore a pretty dress girl
5. —, second, third first
6. David put on a clean — shirt

ur { **hurl** **curls** **curtain** **turn** **burnt** **turkey** }

7. Elizabeth had — in her hair curls
8. Move around turn
9. If you play with fire you may be — burnt
10. It hangs at the window curtains
11. At Christmas we often eat — turkey
12. To throw hurl

sh

shell	shoes	ship
shop	shelf	sharp

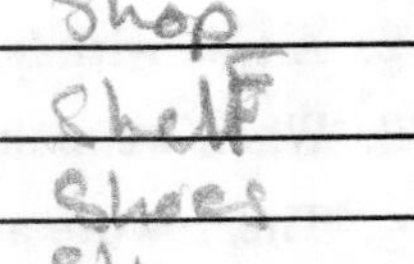

1. We buy sweets from the — ________
2. For putting things on ________
3. Worn on the feet ________
4. It sails across the sea ________

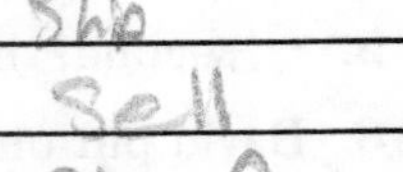

5. A snail has one on its back ________
6. A pin has a — point ________

ch { chat chop chin chips chest church }

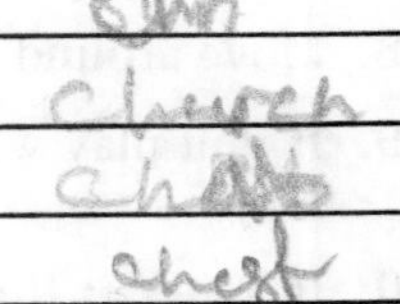

7. A part of the face ________
8. A building ________
9. A friendly talk ________
10. A big box ________
11. You — wood with an axe ________
12. Often eaten with fish ________

bee beech deer
see steel peel

1. An animal with big horns ________
2. A strong metal ________
3. The name of a tree ________

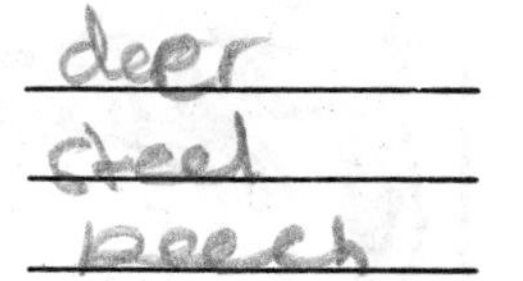

4. The skin of an orange or lemon ________

5. It makes honey for us ________
6. We — with our eyes ________

oo { pools wood soot
shoot good stoop }

7. Black and found in chimneys ________
8. To bend forward ________

9. Lots of trees ________
10. To fire a gun ________

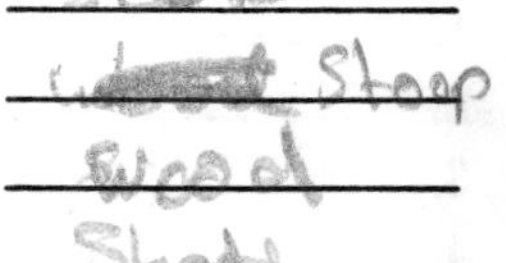

11. Not bad ________
12. The rain makes these ________

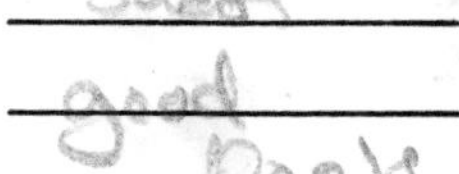

Eaten

cheese	celery	bread	toast
butter	grapes	apples	
buns	cabbage	carrots	

1. bread
2. suticace
3. plants
4. upple
5. Cheese
6. Grape
7.
8.
9.
10. Carrots

Score

ai

tail	chain	wait
rain	drain	pain

1. Water from the clouds ___rain___
2. Rings of metal joined together ___chain___
3. I will — for my Mum to come back ___wait___
4. A dog wags its — ___tail___
5. Water runs into a — ___drain___
6. We sometimes have a — when we are poorly ___pain___

ea

sea	team	easy
tea	hear	tears

7. There are 11 footballers in a — ___team___
8. We — with our ears ___hear___
9. We pour this from a pot ___tea___
10. These come when we cry ___tears___
11. Ships sail across the — ___sea___
12. Not hard ___easy___

oa

boat	soap	road
oats	goals	coat

1. Footballers try to score — goals
2. Motor-cars travel on the — Road
3. Something we wear coat
4. Used for washing our hands soap
5. A small ship boat
6. Horses like to eat — oats

oi { soil oil boil coins join point }

7. A kettle is used to — water boil
8. Money, but not banknotes coin
9. A needle has a sharp — point
10. Fasten together oil
11. Put — on your bicycle to make it go better join
12. Plants grow in the — soil

ou

out round shout
hour found clouds

1. Dark ones often bring rain ______
2. To speak in a very loud voice ______
3. David — a present near his bed ______
4. Not in ______
5. Sixty minutes are the same as one — ______
6. The shape of a ring ______

ay { days pray May
lays play hay }

7. A hen — eggs ______
8. Horses eat — ______
9. After lessons we go out to — ______
10. To say prayers ______
11. The fifth month of the year ______
12. There are seven — in a week ______

ack

back Jack sack black

1. Father Christmas carries a — ____________

2. You lean — in your seat ____________

3. A boy's name ____________

4. A colour ____________

eck { deck neck pecks speck

5. A bird does this ____________

6. A part of the body ____________

7. A sailor walks on the — ____________

8. A tiny bit ____________

ick { pick lick chick sick

9. Poorly ____________

10. A baby bird ____________

11. Tom was told to — up the suitcase ____________

12. On hot days it is fun to — an icecream ____________

Worn

shoe	sock	jersey	glove
beret	sandal	jeans	
scarf	blazer	dressing-gown	

1. ______________ 6. ______________
2. ______________ 7. ______________
3. ______________ 8. ______________
4. ______________ 9. ______________
5. ______________ 10. ______________

Score

ock

rock lock sock cock

1. A key fits into this ____________
2. Worn on the foot ____________
3. A father bird ____________
4. A big stone ____________

uck { luck suck stuck duck

5. The baby began to — his bottle ____________
6. I wish you good — ____________
7. The name of a bird ____________
8. John — the stamp on the letter ____________

ang { rang gang sang hang

9. A group of people ____________
10. The blackbird — sweetly ____________
11. The bell — loudly ____________
12. Let's — the picture on this wall ____________

ing

ring king sting wings

1. Wasps and bees can do this ______
2. It is worn on a finger ______
3. He wears a crown ______
4. For flying ______

ong: long, belong, songs, among

5. We sing these ______
6. A rabbit has — ears ______
7. She sat — the other girls ______
8. Does this hat — to you? ______

ung: sung, rung, hung, stung

9. Elizabeth was — by a wasp ______
10. The bell was — at four o'clock ______
11. The wet shirt — on the line ______
12. Have they — their song? ______

—e

cane	tape	sale
lane	gale	fade

1. A narrow road ____________
2. A strong wind ____________
3. The sun makes the colours in the curtains — ____________
4. Things are cheaper in a — ____________
5. A narrow strip of cloth ____________
6. A thin stick ____________

—e { dive pile side wipe ride time }

7. To rub with a cloth ____________
8. To go headfirst into water ____________
9. What — will tea be ready, Mum? ____________
10. Jill can — a horse ____________
11. A heap ____________
12. Our garage stands at the — of the house ____________

hole	robe	sole
bone	pole	poke

1. The bottom of your shoe ______________
2. A long piece of wood ______________
3. A long dress ______________
4. A mouse lives in a — ______________
5. To push your finger into something ______________
6. A dog likes a — ______________

—e

tube	true	tune
blue	glue	flute

7. Used to stick things ______________
8. Jim hummed a little — to himself ______________
9. I like — stories best ______________
10. We squeeze toothpaste from a — ______________
11. The tune was played on a — ______________
12. A colour ______________

Help in the kitchen

table	mother	mixing bowl	
rolling-pin	scales	apron	
milk	kettle	kitten	cooker

1. ____________
2. ____________
3. ____________
4. ____________
5. ____________
6. ____________
7. ____________
8. ____________
9. ____________
10. ____________

Score

Months

May	March	November	October
June	July	September	January
April	August	December	February

1. What is the first month of the year? __________
2. second __________
3. third __________
4. fourth __________
5. fifth __________
6. sixth __________
7. seventh __________
8. eighth __________
9. ninth __________
10. tenth __________
11. eleventh __________
12. twelfth __________

tt

hitting	scatter	clatter	
pretty	mutter	fatter	cotton

1. Used with a needle ______
2. The sound cups and saucers make ______
3. Nice to look at ______
4. Bigger and rounder ______
5. To throw all over the place ______
6. To speak in a low voice ______
7. Smacking ______

wa { was wasp war water
wash swan watch wants }

8. Fighting between armies ______
9. To clean with water ______
10. A large graceful bird ______
11. Like a bee and it stings ______
12. I did not know I — late ______
13. Used for telling the time ______
14. Mary — a doll for Christmas ______
15. A drink ______

qu

quick	quite	queer	quarter	quiet

1. Strange ____________
2. ¼ ____________
3. Fast ____________
4. Not noisy ____________
5. He told her that Christopher was — a clever boy ____________

ie | chief field piece friend shields

6. Knights carried them ____________
7. Another word for a part ____________
8. A word meaning the leader ____________
9. A farmer puts his animals into this ____________
10. A pal ____________

ui | suit fruit bruise juice biscuit

11. A dark patch on the skin ____________
12. The — from an orange is lovely to drink ____________
13. Apples, oranges and grapes are all different kinds of — ____________
14. Often eaten with a cup of tea ____________
15. The rain had spoilt a — of clothes ____________

Days

Tuesday	Saturday	Wednesday	Thursday	Monday

1. It comes after Wednesday ________
2. The day after Friday ________
3. On Pancake — we eat pancakes ________
4. The day before Tuesday ________
5. The day before Thursday ________

oy { boy annoy enjoy toys oyster }

6. Father Christmas seems to bring lots of these. ________
7. To tease ________
8. A shellfish ________
9. Not a girl but a — ________
10. To have a good time ________

ept { wept kept swept slept crept }

11. Went on sleeping ________
12. Did not give away ________
13. I — quietly upstairs to bed ________
14 Cried ________
15. Used a sweeping brush ________

Fun on the beach

pier	lighthouse	seagull	
boat	bucket	spade	sand-castle
towel	seaweed	swimsuit	

1. ______________________
2. ______________________
3. ______________________
4. ______________________
5. ______________________
6. ______________________
7. ______________________
8. ______________________
9. ______________________
10. ______________________

Score

e { bake rake wake behave care tame share }

1. A garden tool ______
2. A tiger is wild, but a dog is — ______
3. Always take — when crossing a road ______
4. Cook ______
5. Sh! Don't — the baby ______
6. If you — yourself, you may stay up late ______
7. A part of something ______

~~e~~ + ing { baking raking caring sharing taming waking having behaving }

8. Many children are good at — their sweets with others ______
9. Taking care ______
10. Opening your eyes after sleep ______
11. Making a wild animal less wild ______
12. Using a rake ______
13. The class was — well ______
14. Cooking ______
15. Ian is — a birthday party ______

e

ride	dine	hide	dive
ice	like	wipe	

1. To travel on a horse is to — it ____________
2. Frozen water ____________
3. To go down headfirst ____________
4. To eat your dinner ____________
5. Rub with a cloth ____________
6. To keep out of sight ____________
7. I — icecream ____________

e̸ + ing { dining riding hiding diving icing liking wiping giving }

8. Keeping out of sight ____________
9. Made of sugar ____________
10. Travelling on horseback ____________
11. Dinner was in the — room ____________
12. The teacher was — out books ____________
13. Rubbing with a cloth ____________
14. Going headfirst into water ____________
15. Enjoying ____________

poke	doze	hope	
joke	store	love	come

1. I — it will stop raining ________
2. Can you — out to play? ________
3. A light sleep ________
4. It hurts to — a finger in your eye ________
5. A trick ________
6. I would — to have a holiday ________
7. Tins of food are often kept in a — cupboard ________

¢ + ing { poking hoping dozing joking storing boring loving coming }

8. My friend is — to tea ________
9. Playing tricks ________
10. Kate is — for snow tomorrow ________
11. Dull and not interesting ________
12. Kind ________
13. Simon was — a stick into the hole ________
14. Having a light sleep ________
15. Putting things away until later ________

e

tune	tube	cure	prune	use

1. Toothpaste is sold in a — ________
2. The doctor found a — for the disease ________
3. My Dad taught me to — a saw ________
4. It's a song with a merry — ________
5. A dried plum ________

e̸ + ing { using tubing pruning tuning curing

6. Inside a tyre there is rubber — ________
7. Dr. Brown is — the lad of his spots ________
8. Mrs Jones is — her washing machine ________
9. Father was busy — the roses ________
10. An old man was — our piano ________

ff { toffee coffee stiff staff off

11. The light was switched — ________
12. The teachers at a school ________
13. A sticky sweet ________
14. A drink ________
15. Does not bend ________

Birthday party

cards	balloons	cake	candles
paper hat	presents	cracker	
clock	sideboard	toffees	

1. ____________________
2. ____________________
3. ____________________
4. ____________________
5. ____________________
6. ____________________
7. ____________________
8. ____________________
9. ____________________
10. ____________________

Score

Numbers

two	four	seven	one
six	five	three	

1. $7 - 6$ __________
2. $8 \div 4$ __________
3. $9 \div 3$ __________
4. 2×2 __________
5. Half a dozen __________
6. $2 + 3$ __________
7. $4 + 3$ __________

aw { paw saw draw law
jaw raw hawk straw }

8. To make a picture with a pencil __________
9. A part of the face __________
10. A dog's foot __________
11. Not cooked __________
12. A tool used for cutting wood __________
13. Animals sleep on it __________
14. A bird __________
15. Parking on a zebra crossing is against the — __________

mm

summer	mummy	dummy	
slammed	drummer	hammer	tummy

1. We like to fill this with food ______
2. Only a baby would suck this ______
3. Mother ______
4. After the spring comes the — ______
5. A tool for hitting nails ______
6. He plays the drums ______
7. Shut with a bang ______

nn { pinned grinned running cunning
winner winning dinner thinner }

8. If Arthur came first he was the — ______
9. If you don't eat you will grow — ______
10. The main meal of the day ______
11. Fastened with a pin ______
12. Faster than walking ______
13. Sly ______
14. For — the race his aunt gave him a present ______
15. Tom — all over his face ______

y

fairy	many	daisy	
baby	diary	berry	lady

1. A flower ____________
2. A fruit ____________
3. A tiny child ____________
4. A book you write in ____________
5. A woman ____________
6. Often at the top of a Christmas tree ____________
7. A lot ____________

kn { knot knew knits knee
knock knight knife kneel }

8. A sharp tool ____________
9. He rode on horseback ____________
10. Hit ____________
11. You tie this ____________
12. Mary — all her tables ____________
13. To go down on your knees ____________
14. A part of the leg ____________
15. Mother does it with two needles ____________

ies

fairies	lollies	daisies	
babies	diaries	ladies	berries

1. Sweets ____________
2. Tiny children ____________
3. Fruits ____________
4. Flowers ____________
5. These are supposed to live in 'Fairyland' ____________
6. Women ____________
7. Books in which we write what happens ____________

all { tall stall ball all
wall hall call fall }

8. Everyone ____________
9. Tumble ____________
10. The — was packed for the meeting ____________
11. Built of bricks and cement ____________
12. Shout ____________
13. A kind of shop in a market ____________
14. It is round and used in games ____________
15. High ____________

Spring-cleaning

saddle	handlebars	spokes	
tyre	mudguard	handpump	
oilcan	spanner	chain	pedal

1. ______________________
2. ______________________
3. ______________________
4. ______________________
5. ______________________
6. ______________________
7. ______________________
8. ______________________
9. ______________________
10. ______________________

Score

x

six axe boxes
wax sixty foxes sixteen

1. A candle is made of this ______
2. 6 ______
3. 16 ______
4. 60 ______
5. For putting things in ______
6. Animals with bushy tails ______
7. Used for chopping down trees ______

ea { head bread dead meadow
breath lead read weather }

8. Not alive ______
9. The air we breathe out is our — ______
10. At six we heard the — forecast ______
11. A food made from flour ______
12. John put his cap on his — ______
13. The teacher — us a story ______
14. A field of grass ______
15. A very heavy metal ______

ied

tried	fried	cried	lied	died

1. Shed tears ____________
2. Cooked in a frying pan ____________
3. Worked very hard ____________
4. Did not live ____________
5. Did not tell the truth ____________

le { thistle freckle little handle prickle
candle bottle rifle trifle rattle }

6. Milk comes in this ____________
7. Small ____________
8. A baby's plaything ____________
9. A prickly weed ____________
10. A gooseberry bush has many a sharp one ____________
11. Open the door with this ____________
12. A brown mark on the face ____________
13. Often eaten at a party ____________
14. It gives us light ____________
15. A gun carried by soldiers ____________

face	ace	trace	
lace	race	place	pace

1. Used to tie your shoe ______
2. To go fast ______
3. A step or stride ______
4. To go over the lines with a pencil ______
5. Show me the — where it hurts ______
6. The front part of the head ______
7. The 'one' in a pack of cards ______

bb { rubber cobbler rubbing bubbles robber pebble wobble

8. A boy's name ______
9. If you — on a bicycle you may fall off ______
10. Small children blow these ______
11. A small stone ______
12. He mends shoes ______
13. A thief ______
14. It takes out pencil marks ______
15. Polishing ______

ight

fight	light	night	
sight	might	right	tight

1. Turn left not — ______
2. The dark hours ______
3. A battle ______
4. His shoes hurt because they were too — ______
5. The trees and lakes were a lovely — ______
6. At night we switch on the — ______
7. 'It — snow tomorrow,' said Jane ______

Pets: rabbit, kitten, canary, goldfish, parrot, mouse, horse, budgerigar

8. A yellow singing bird ______
9. A fish ______
10. A young cat ______
11. A big bird which often talks ______
12. This lives in a hutch ______
13. His short name is 'budgie' ______
14. The biggest of them all ______
15. A small animal with a long tail ______

Trouble at the supermarket

toddler   cereal packet   old gentleman

walking stick   assistant   tinned fruit

basket   handbag   loaf   coffee

1. ____________________   6. ____________________

2. ____________________   7. ____________________

3. ____________________   8. ____________________

4. ____________________   9. ____________________

5. ____________________   10. ____________________

Score

wh

whip	which	whisper	
wheel	whale	white	wheat

1. A huge sea-creature ____________
2. The colour of snow ____________
3. A lion-trainer may use one ____________
4. To talk very softly ____________
5. A car carries a spare one ____________
6. Flour is made from this ____________
7. A word often used when asking questions ____________

Buildings { office house hotel station
school garage church hospital }

8. A building for a car ____________
9. Papers and typewriters are found here ____________
10. A place to stay on our holidays perhaps ____________
11. God's house ____________
12. We learn our lessons here ____________
13. Ill people often go here ____________
14. The building we live in ____________
15. Trains stop at this ____________

The Body

eyes	knee	throat	mouth	knuckle
ears	wrist	ankle	fingers	shoulder
hair	head	thumb	elbow	eyebrows

1. We have eight of these and two thumbs ______
2. A joint in the arm ______
3. A joint halfway down the leg ______
4. Where the brain is ______
5. A part of the finger ______
6. Hairs just above the eyes ______
7. Used for listening ______
8. Used for seeing ______
9. This grows on the head ______
10. The tongue and the teeth are in this ______
11. Used for swallowing ______
12. This joins the hand and the arm ______
13. Where the arm joins the body ______
14. We have one on each hand ______
15. This joint helps us to move our foot ______

canal	final	metal	animal
petal	signal	sandal	hospital

1. Engine drivers look out for this ____________
2. A kind of shoe ____________
3. A building for people who are ill ____________
4. A four-legged creature ____________
5. A waterway ____________
6. A word meaning last ____________
7. Made of iron and steel ____________
8. Part of a flower ____________

Numbers { eight, eleven, twelve, nineteen, twenty, fifteen, thirteen }

9. 11 ____________
10. A dozen ____________
11. 4×2 ____________
12. A score ____________
13. 5×3 ____________
14. 19 ____________
15. 13 ____________

el

models	kennel	chapel	quarrel	
travel	parcel	shovel	angel	tunnel

1. A church ________
2. A tool ________
3. Package brought by the postman ________
4. Children make these from wood and cardboard ________
5. A home for a dog ________
6. An underground passage ________
7. To argue angrily ________
8. Move from one place to another ________
9. A messenger from God ________

str { straw street strict stream straight stranger

10. A person not known to you ________
11. A road in a town ________
12. Stalks from corn ________
13. A small river ________
14. Stern ________
15. Not crooked ________

The quarrel

poodle	fox terrier	lead	
collar	pavement	kerb	manhole cover
pillar-box	trilby hat	policeman	

1. ______________________
2. ______________________
3. ______________________
4. ______________________
5. ______________________
6. ______________________
7. ______________________
8. ______________________
9. ______________________
10. ______________________

Score

gu

guitar guide guest guard guilty

1. A visitor to your home ____________
2. Protect ____________
3. Having done something wrong ____________
4. A musical instrument ____________
5. One who shows the way ____________

ough | cough enough rough tough

6. Strong ____________
7. Plenty ____________
8. Not smooth ____________
9. Often follows a cold ____________

air | pair aircraft upstairs
dairy fairies repair

10. Aeroplanes ____________
11. Plural of 'fairy' ____________
12. A shop which sells milk ____________
13. Two of the same kind ____________
14. Peter went — in his dressing gown ____________
15. A word meaning mend ____________

ur

further	purple	curved	burn	Saturday
return	surprise	burglar	turnip	Thursday

1. Go back ____________
2. He robs houses and shops ____________
3. A vegetable ____________
4. If today is Tuesday the day after tomorrow will be — ____________
5. Put in the fire ____________
6. A colour ____________
7. A word meaning farther ____________
8. Bent ____________
9. An unexpected happening ____________
10. The last day of the week ____________

ying

dying drying flying frying trying

11. Cooking ____________
12. Moving through the air ____________
13. Working hard ____________
14. Losing life ____________
15. Getting rid of the water ____________

ves

halves	wives	leaves	thieves	wolves
calves	loaves	knives	shelves	themselves

1. Married women ______________
2. Used for putting things on ______________
3. For cutting ______________
4. The teacher told them to behave — ______________
5. Farm animals ______________
6. Wild animals ______________
7. People who steal ______________
8. In the autumn they are swept up ______________
9. Cakes of bread ______________
10. Two — make a whole one ______________

ion { nation, relation, portion, direction, mention }

11. The horse galloped in that — ______________
12. A people ______________
13. A member of your family ______________
14. A part ______________
15. To speak about ______________

tch

watch	ditch	pitch	matches	scratches
fetch	itches	stretch	kitchen	stitches
hutch	switch	witch	butcher	patch

1. We buy our meat from him ______________
2. Martin needed three — in his leg ______________
3. A piece of cloth to cover a hole ______________
4. A cat's claws will leave these on your skin ______________
5. When struck they burn ______________
6. A room for cooking and washing up the pots ______________
7. To bring ______________
8. To pull out and make longer ______________
9. A trench for water ______________
10. She is said to ride on a broomstick ______________
11. A house for a rabbit ______________
12. Tickles ______________
13. The team rolled the cricket — ______________
14. It puts on the light ______________
15. It gives us the time ______________

Help in the garden

greenhouse	fence	wheelbarrow
leaves	rake	sundial	bonfire
trowel	sunflowers	rockery

1. ______________ 6. ______________
2. ______________ 7. ______________
3. ______________ 8. ______________
4. ______________ 9. ______________
5. ______________ 10. ______________

Score

rr

purrs	narrow	worried	carriage	marriage
arrow	hurries	arrange	porridge	tomorrow
error	mirror	arrested	arrived	strawberries

1. Shot from a bow ____________
2. A wedding ____________
3. For carrying people ____________
4. A breakfast food made from oats ____________
5. To put things in order ____________
6. The day which comes after today ____________
7. The gate was too — for the tractor ____________
8. If a cat —, it is happy ____________
9. Troubled about something ____________
10. Goes quickly ____________
11. Fruit ____________
12. A looking-glass ____________
13. Caught by the police ____________
14. The Scouts — home wet through ____________
15. A mistake ____________

or

cork	pork	forty	
worm	forgets	snore	fortnight

1. It makes holes in the soil ________
2. Do you — when you are asleep? ________
3. Fits into a bottle ________
4. 20 × 2 ________
5. Meat from a pig ________
6. Does not remember ________
7. Fourteen days ________

or

motor	sailor	doctor	corridor
actor	junior	tractor	emperor

8. A passage ________
9. A person who acts ________
10. A child under about 11 years of age ________
11. Farmers use it when ploughing the fields ________
12. An engine ________
13. We go to him when we are ill ________
14. A seaman ________
15. A king who roles over an empire ________

wr

wrist	wrong	wrapped	
wreck	wriggle	wrinkles	writing

1. It joins the arm to the hand ____________
2. His mother was — a letter ____________
3. To twist and turn ____________
4. A ship broken up by the sea ____________
5. Covered in paper ____________
6. Small lines on the face ____________
7. Not right ____________

ey { money honey chimney monkey donkey

8. An animal rather like a man ____________
9. For the smoke to go up ____________
10. Coins ____________
11. A sweet food ____________
12. Like a horse, but has long ears ____________

eight { weight height eight

13. How high a thing is ____________
14. 8 ____________
15. How heavy a thing is ____________

ce

twice	palace	saucer	piece	policeman
iceberg	grocer	notice	peace	lettuce

1. A house for a king ______
2. A large floating lump of ice ______
3. A teacup stands on this ______
4. A part of something ______
5. He keeps order ______
6. Two times ______
7. A shopkeeper ______
8. Often pinned up on a board to be read ______
9. Quietness ______
10. Vegetable used in salads ______

nch { lunch finch branch ranch pinch

11. The arm of a tree ______
12. A bird ______
13. To nip ______
14. A meal ______
15. Cowboys are found on this ______

At the circus

whip	ringmaster	bareback rider	
clown	bucket	umbrella	acrobat
trapeze	tightrope walker	juggler	

1. ____________________
2. ____________________
3. ____________________
4. ____________________
5. ____________________
6. ____________________
7. ____________________
8. ____________________
9. ____________________
10. ____________________

Score

roller	called	collar	yellow	swallow
silly	really	willow	tallest	woollen
till	ballet	follow	village	William

1. A boy's name ____________
2. Foolish ____________
3. A tree ____________
4. Shops keep their money in this ____________
5. A colour ____________
6. A dog wears one round the neck ____________
7. A boy — Jonathan scored two goals ____________
8. Truly ____________
9. To come after ____________
10. A bird ____________
11. A place not big enough to be a town ____________
12. Made of wool ____________
13. A word meaning the highest ____________
14. Dancing to music on a stage ____________
15. A garden tool ____________

ck

struck	wicked	kicked	stockings
pockets	jacket	rockets	blackboard
cricket	pickle	chicken	mackintosh

1. They fire these into the air ____________
2. A summer game ____________
3. A farm bird ____________
4. Evil ____________
5. A raincoat ____________
6. It adds a tang to food ____________
7. A word meaning hit ____________
8. A short coat ____________
9. Hit with the foot ____________
10. Chalk is used to write on this ____________
11. Worn on the legs ____________
12. In coats and trousers for carrying things in ____________

tele { telephone, telescope, television

13. The short name is TV ____________
14. Used for studying the stars ____________
15. Used for speaking to people ____________

ly

tidily	loudly	safely	happily	suddenly
slowly	bravely	easily	kindly	honestly
quietly	sadly	gently	poorly	lovely

1. All at once ____________
2. Beautiful ____________
3. Full of happiness ____________
4. Taking a long time ____________
5. Neatly ____________
6. In a loud way ____________
7. Without difficulty ____________
8. In a kind way ____________
9. Without much sound ____________
10. In a safe way ____________
11. Truthfully ____________
12. In a gentle manner ____________
13. In bad health ____________
14. In a sad way ____________
15. With courage ____________

dresses	princess	assist	useless	address
pressed	illness	glasses	passage	messenger

1. We drink out of these ______
2. Worn by girls ______
3. Daughter of a king or queen ______
4. A corridor ______
5. Help ______
6. It is written on an envelope ______
7. Of no use ______
8. Pushed hard ______
9. Sickness ______
10. One who takes a message ______

mb { bomber plumber climb dumb limbs }

11. Arms and legs ______
12. To go upwards ______
13. A war plane ______
14. Unable to speak ______
15. He repairs pipes and windows ______

Holiday ahead

caravan	roof-rack	rubber dinghy	corgi
sleeping-bag	suitcase	vacuum flask	
beach ball	cricket bat	wellington boots	

1. ______________________
2. ______________________
3. ______________________
4. ______________________
5. ______________________
6. ______________________
7. ______________________
8. ______________________
9. ______________________
10. ______________________

Score

ed

called	sharpened	roared	travelled	listened
entered	fastened	prayed	talked	frightened

1. Fixed ______________
2. Talked to God ______________
3. Used his ears ______________
4. Made a noise like a lion ______________
5. Named ______________
6. Dad — the carving knife ______________
7. Afraid ______________
8. Came in ______________
9. Spoke ______________
10. Moved from one place to another ______________

ful { awful beautiful useful handful careful }

11. Lovely to look at ______________
12. As much as can be held in one hand ______________
13. Not careless ______________
14. Helpful ______________
15. The burning ship was an — sight ______________

pp

supper	clapping	disappear	
hopping	pepper	stopped	disappointed

1. Not moving ______________
2. Going on one foot in jumps ______________
3. A meal ______________
4. Sad ______________
5. To go out of sight ______________
6. It can make you sneeze ______________
7. Striking the hands together ______________

ought | fought ought brought thoughts bought

8. Tom — a lollipop from the shop ______________
9. Ideas ______________
10. We — to visit the dentist twice a year ______________
11. Struggled ______________
12. Fetched ______________

aught | taught caught daughter

13. Captured ______________
14. A girl ______________
15. His fall — him to be careful ______________

Tricky Ones

safety	bicycle	queue	hymns	cupboard
choir	library	yacht	colours	leopard
tongue	theatre	suite	Elizabeth	orchestra

1. Sung in church ________________
2. Place for storing things ________________
3. A girl's name ________________
4. A line of waiting people ________________
5. A set of furniture ________________
6. Plays are acted here ________________
7. A band in a theatre ________________
8. For tasting and talking ________________
9. Cycle with two wheels ________________
10. For sailing ________________
11. A group of singers ________________
12. We borrow books from here ________________
13. His costume was fastened with a — pin ________________
14. Fierce animal in cat family ________________
15. Blue, red, yellow and green ________________

(1)

1. rat
2. bat
3. gas
4. lad
5. hat
6. bag
7. hen
8. bed
9. ten
10. peg
11. pen
12. leg

(2)

1. lip
2. pin
3. tin
4. sit
5. bit
6. hit
7. cot
8. dog
9. fog
10. hop
11. log
12. top

(3)

1. mug
2. hug
3. nut
4. bull
5. rub
6. cub
7. fun
8. dry
9. why
10. try
11. fry
12. cry

(4)

1. jar
2. far
3. star
4. car
5. tar
6. bar
7. flower
8. tower
9. bow
10. owl
11. drown
12. howl

(5)

1. stack
2. barn
3. duck
4. pond
5. tractor
6. cat
7. cock
8. hen
9. goat
10. dog

(6)

1. term
2. fern
3. her
4. jerk
5. stork
6. storm
7. corn
8. born
9. port
10. horns
11. worn
12. form

(7)

1. bird
2. fir
3. stir
4. girl
5. first
6. shirt
7. curls
8. turn
9. burnt
10. curtain
11. turkey
12. hurl

(8)

1. shop
2. shelf
3. shoes
4. ship
5. shell
6. sharp
7. chin
8. church
9. chat
10. chest
11. chop
12. chips

(9)

1. deer
2. steel
3. beech
4. peel
5. bee
6. see
7. soot
8. stoop
9. wood
10. shoot
11. good
12. pools

(10)

1. bread
2. toast
3. celery
4. apples
5. cheese
6. grapes
7. cabbage
8. buns
9. butter
10. carrots

(11)

1. rain
2. chain
3. wait
4. tail
5. drain
6. pain
7. team
8. hear
9. tea
10. tears
11. sea
12. easy

(12)

1. goals
2. road
3. coat
4. soap
5. boat
6. oats
7. boil
8. coins
9. point
10. join
11. oil
12. soil

(13)

1. clouds
2. shout
3. found
4. out
5. hour
6. round
7. lays
8. hay
9. play
10. pray
11. May
12. days

(14)

1. sack
2. back
3. Jack
4. black
5. pecks
6. neck
7. deck
8. speck
9. sick
10. chick
11. pick
12. lick

(15)

1. jersey
2. dressing-gown
3. jeans
4. blazer
5. sandal
6. scarf
7. beret
8. shoe
9. glove
10. sock

(16)

1. lock
2. sock
3. cock
4. rock
5. suck
6. luck
7. duck
8. stuck
9. gang
10. sang
11. rang
12. hang

(17)

1. sting
2. ring
3. king
4. wings
5. songs
6. long
7. among
8. belong
9. stung
10. rung
11. hung
12. sung

(18)

1. lane
2. gale
3. fade
4. sale
5. tape
6. cane
7. wipe
8. dive
9. time
10. ride
11. pile
12. side

(19)

1. sole
2. pole
3. robe
4. hole
5. poke
6. bone
7. glue
8. tune
9. true
10. tube
11. flute
12. blue

(20)

1. kettle
2. cooker
3. mother
4. mixing bowl
5. scales
6. rolling-pin
7. milk
8. table
9. kitten
10. apron

(21)

1. January
2. February
3. March
4. April
5. May
6. June
7. July
8. August
9. September
10. October
11. November
12. December

(22)

1. cotton
2. clatter
3. pretty
4. fatter
5. scatter
6. mutter
7. hitting
8. war
9. wash
10. swan
11. wasp
12. was
13. watch
14. wants
15. water

(23)

1. queer
2. quarter
3. quick
4. quiet
5. quite
6. shields
7. piece
8. chief
9. field
10. friend
11. bruise
12. juice
13. fruit
14. biscuit
15. suit

(24)

1. Thursday
2. Saturday
3. Tuesday
4. Monday
5. Wednesday
6. toys
7. annoy
8. oyster
9. boy
10. enjoy
11. slept
12. kept
13. crept
14. wept
15. swept

(25)

1. lighthouse
2. seagull
3. pier
4. boat
5. towel
6. seaweed
7. sand-castle
8. bucket
9. swimsuit
10. spade

(26)

1. rake
2. tame
3. care
4. bake
5. wake
6. behave
7. share
8. sharing
9. caring
10. waking
11. taming
12. raking
13. behaving
14. baking
15. having

(27)

1. ride
2. ice
3. dive
4. dine
5. wipe
6. hide
7. like
8. hiding
9. icing
10. riding
11. dining
12. giving
13. wiping
14. diving
15. liking

(28)

1. hope
2. come
3. doze
4. poke
5. joke
6. love
7. store
8. coming
9. joking
10. hoping
11. boring
12. loving
13. poking
14. dozing
15. storing

(29)

1. tube
2. cure
3. use
4. tune
5. prune
6. tubing
7. curing
8. using
9. pruning
10. tuning
11. off
12. staff
13. toffee
14. coffee
15. stiff

(30)

1. balloons
2. cards
3. clock
4. paper hat
5. sideboard
6. candles
7. cake
8. toffees
9. cracker
10. presents

(31)

1. one
2. two
3. three
4. four
5. six
6. five
7. seven
8. draw
9. jaw
10. paw
11. raw
12. saw
13. straw
14. hawk
15. law

(32)

1. tummy
2. dummy
3. mummy
4. summer
5. hammer
6. drummer
7. slammed
8. winner
9. thinner
10. dinner
11. pinned
12. running
13. cunning
14. winning
15. grinned

(33)

1. daisy
2. berry
3. baby
4. diary
5. lady
6. fairy
7. many
8. knife
9. knight
10. knock
11. knot
12. knew
13. kneel
14. knee
15. knits

(34)

1. lollies
2. babies
3. berries
4. daisies
5. fairies
6. ladies
7. diaries
8. all
9. fall
10. hall
11. wall
12. call
13. stall
14. ball
15. tall

(35)

1. saddle
2. handlebars
3. spokes
4. chain
5. pedal
6. tyre
7. spanner
8. mudguard
9. oilcan
10. handpump

(36)

1. wax
2. six
3. sixteen
4. sixty
5. boxes
6. foxes
7. axe
8. dead
9. breath
10. weather
11. bread
12. head
13. read
14. meadow
15. lead

(37)

1. cried
2. fried
3. tried
4. died
5. lied
6. bottle
7. little
8. rattle
9. thistle
10. prickle
11. handle
12. freckle
13. trifle
14. candle
15. rifle

(38)

1. lace
2. race
3. pace
4. trace
5. place
6. face
7. ace
8. Bobby
9. wobble
10. bubbles
11. pebble
12. cobbler
13. robber
14. rubber
15. rubbing

(39)

1. right
2. night
3. fight
4. tight
5. sight
6. light
7. might
8. canary
9. goldfish
10. kitten
11. parrot
12. rabbit
13. budgerigar
14. horse
15. mouse

(40)

1. tinned fruit
2. assistant
3. old gentleman
4. walking stick
5. toddler
6. cereal packet
7. handbag
8. coffee
9. basket
10. loaf

(41)

1. whale
2. white
3. whip
4. whisper
5. wheel
6. wheat
7. which
8. garage
9. office
10. hotel
11. church
12. school
13. hospital
14. house
15. station

(42)

1. fingers
2. elbow
3. knee
4. head
5. knuckle
6. eyebrows
7. ears
8. eyes
9. hair
10. mouth
11. throat
12. wrist
13. shoulder
14. thumb
15. ankle

(43)

1. signal
2. sandal
3. hospital
4. animal
5. canal
6. final
7. metal
8. petal
9. eleven
10. twelve
11. eight
12. twenty
13. fifteen
14. nineteen
15. thirteen

(44)

1. chapel
2. shovel
3. parcel
4. models
5. kennel
6. tunnel
7. quarrel
8. travel
9. angel
10. stranger
11. street
12. straw
13. stream
14. strict
15. straight

(45)

1. trilby hat
2. policeman
3. pillar-box
4. manhole cover
5. lead
6. collar
7. pavement
8. fox terrier
9. kerb
10. poodle

(46)

1. guest
2. guard
3. guilty
4. guitar
5. guide
6. tough
7. enough
8. rough
9. cough
10. aircraft
11. fairies
12. dairy
13. pair
14. upstairs
15. repair

(47)

1. return
2. burglar
3. turnip
4. Thursday
5. burn
6. purple
7. further
8. curved
9. surprise
10. Saturday
11. frying
12. flying
13. trying
14. dying
15. drying

(48)

1. wives
2. shelves
3. knives
4. themselves
5. calves
6. wolves
7. thieves
8. leaves
9. loaves
10. halves
11. direction
12. nation
13. relation
14. portion
15. mention

(49)

1. butcher
2. stitches
3. patch
4. scratches
5. matches
6. kitchen
7. fetch
8. stretch
9. ditch
10. witch
11. hutch
12. itches
13. pitch
14. switch
15. watch

(50)

1. greenhouse
2. sunflowers
3. fence
4. rake
5. bonfire
6. wheelbarrow
7. leaves
8. rockery
9. sundial
10. trowel

(51)

1. arrow
2. marriage
3. carriage
4. porridge
5. arrange
6. tomorrow
7. narrow
8. purrs
9. worried
10. hurries
11. strawberries
12. mirror
13. arrested
14. arrived
15. error

(52)

1. worm
2. snore
3. cork
4. forty
5. pork
6. forgets
7. fortnight
8. corridor
9. actor
10. junior
11. tractor
12. motor
13. doctor
14. sailor
15. emperor

(53)

1. wrist
2. writing
3. wriggle
4. wreck
5. wrapped
6. wrinkles
7. wrong
8. monkey
9. chimney
10. money
11. honey
12. donkey
13. height
14. eight
15. weight

(54)

1. palace
2. iceberg
3. saucer
4. piece
5. policeman
6. twice
7. grocer
8. notice
9. peace
10. lettuce
11. branch
12. finch
13. pinch
14. lunch
15. ranch

(55)

1. trapeze
2. umbrella
3. bareback rider
4. tightrope walker
5. acrobat
6. juggler
7. clown
8. bucket
9. whip
10. ringmaster

(56)

1. William
2. silly
3. willow
4. till
5. yellow
6. collar
7. called
8. really
9. follow
10. swallow
11. village
12. woollen
13. tallest
14. ballet
15. roller

(57)

1. rockets
2. cricket
3. chicken
4. wicked
5. mackintosh
6. pickle
7. struck
8. jacket
9. kicked
10. blackboard
11. stockings
12. pockets
13. television
14. telescope
15. telephone

(58)

1. suddenly
2. lovely
3. happily
4. slowly
5. tidily
6. loudly
7. easily
8. kindly
9. quietly
10. safely
11. honestly
12. gently
13. poorly
14. sadly
15. bravely

(59)

1. glasses
2. dresses
3. princess
4. passage
5. assist
6. address
7. useless
8. pressed
9. illness
10. messenger
11. limbs
12. climb
13. bomber
14. dumb
15. plumber

(60)

1. roof-rack
2. caravan
3. vacuum flask
4. sleeping-bag
5. rubber dinghy
6. suitcase
7. beach ball
8. cricket bat
9. wellington boots
10. corgi

(61)

1. fastened
2. prayed
3. listened
4. roared
5. called
6. sharpened
7. frightened
8. entered
9. talked
10. travelled
11. beautiful
12. handful
13. careful
14. useful
15. awful

(62)

1. stopped
2. hopping
3. supper
4. disappointed
5. disappear
6. pepper
7. clapping
8. bought
9. thoughts
10. ought
11. fought
12. brought
13. caught
14. daughter
15. taught

(63)

1. hymns
2. cupboard
3. Elizabeth
4. queue
5. suite
6. theatre
7. orchestra
8. tongue
9. bicycle
10. yacht
11. choir
12. library
13. safety
14. leopard
15. colours